NELSON EQAO GRADE 6

Reading and Writing

NELSON

This workbook belongs to:

NELSON

ISBN-13: 978-0-17-688602-8
ISBN-10: 0-17-688602-8

Printed and bound in Canada
1 2 3 4 21 20 19 18

For more information contact Nelson Education Ltd., 1120 Birchmount Road, Toronto, Ontario M1K 5G4. Or you can visit our website at nelson.com.

Credits

Photos
cover: Hero Images/Getty Images
6: Sabphoto/Shutterstock.com; 7: Patricia Marks/Shutterstock.com; 8: Jaren Jai Wicklund/Shutterstock.com; 9: kryzhov/Shutterstock.com; 16: Igor Sinkov/Shutterstock.com; 17: (top) supertramp88/Shutterstock.com, (bottom) Everett Historical/Shutterstock.com; 18: Monkey Business Images/Shutterstock.com; 19: (top) nrqemi/Shutterstock.com, (bottom) Deborah Crowle; 20: Photo smile/Shutterstock.com; 21: thanatphoto/Shutterstock.com; 28: Joseph Sohm/Shutterstock.com; 29: sdecoret/Shutterstock.com; 30: JeniFoto/Shutterstock.com; 31: Digital Storm/Shutterstock.com; 36: Vince Streano/Corbis Documentary/Getty Images; 37: Alana McCarthy/Three In A Box; 38: IgorZh/Shutterstock.com; 39: Tatiana Popova/Shutterstock.com; 44: Aphelleon/Shutterstock.com; 45: NASA Marshall Space Flight Center (NASA-MSFC); 46: Roger Ressmeyer/NASA; 47: (lego) patat/Shutterstock.com, (winter gloves) Boris Sosnovyy/Shutterstock.com; 52: FloridaStock/Shutterstock.com; 53: Illustrated by Deborah Crowle; 54: Rich Carey/Shutterstock.com; 55: Phovoir/Shutterstock.com; 60–63: (all illustrations) Helen Flook; 69–71: (all illustrations) Matt Roussel/Three In A Box; 76: (c) Mary Evans Picture Library/The Image Works; 78: Notman Photographic Archives, McCord Museum, Montreal/MP-0000.909.4; 79: Library and Archives Canada / C-014115; 85: Hogan Imaging/Shutterstock.com; 87: Brent Hofacker/Shutterstock.com; 92: wavebreakmedia/Shutterstock.com; 93: Jaromir Chalabala/Shutterstock.com; 94: nadianb/Shutterstock.com; 95: istetiana/Shutterstock.com; 102: sirtravelalot/Shutterstock.com; 103: Anna Azimi/Shutterstock.com; 104: Roylee_photosunday/Shutterstock.com; 105: VanoVasaio/Shutterstock.com.

Text
6–9: © Nelson Education; 16–21: © Nelson Education; 28–31: © Nelson Education; 36–39: From Flight Balloons, Airships, Kites and Gliders by June Loves, Macmillan Education, 2000. Reprinted by permission of the author; 44–47: © Nelson Education; 52–55: © Nelson Education; 60–63: Rowena Sommerville; 68–71: Peg Kehret, "Little Red, The Hood" from Winning Monologs for Young Actors, by Peg Kehret, © copyright 1986 Meriwether Publishing Ltd. Used by permission of Pioneer Drama Service.; 76–79: Laura Morgan, From "The First Spike" by Laura Morgan, Beginnings: Stories of Canada's Past edited by Ann Walsh (c) 2001. Published by Ronsdale Press. Used with permission.; 84–87: Copyright © Highlights for Children, Inc., Columbus, Ohio. All rights reserved.; 92–95: © Nelson Education; 102–105: © Nelson Education.

Contents

About the EQAO Test

What is EQAO testing?

In Ontario, children in Grades 3, 6, and 9 are required to take a test to assess their literacy skills. The Education Quality and Accountability Office (EQAO) is responsible for this provincial assessment program. The literacy assessments consist of multiple-choice and open-response questions that cover the Ontario language curriculum for reading and writing.

The *Nelson EQAO Grade 6 Reading and Writing Workbook* is designed to provide students with the opportunity to answer the types of questions they will encounter on the EQAO assessment. This book covers the reading and writing skills your child is learning in school.

At Nelson, we believe in empowering every child with the tools to be successful. This is why we work with respected educators across Canada to develop resources that are aligned to provincial curricula and support the learning journey in school and at home.

How can I help prepare my child for EQAO testing?

The *Nelson EQAO Grade 6 Reading and Writing Workbook* features reading selections and two types of questions: multiple choice and open response. Your child will read a short selection and then answer multiple-choice and open-response questions for that selection. These questions will help your child become more comfortable with the EQAO test format.

Open-response questions require both short and long written answers that assess your child's ability to both read and write. Their responses should demonstrate how well they can communicate their ideas, as well as the content of those ideas. That is, many of the questions require your child to show comprehension of the reading selection. Other questions will use the selection as a springboard, requiring a thoughtful written response to a creative writing prompt.

Sample answers are provided for many of the open-response questions. For other questions, suggested criteria are included for what a good answer will look like.

In addition, to help your child prepare for the EQAO test, you might want to review the tips on page 118 together.

REWARD CONTRACT

When you complete a test in your *Nelson EQAO Grade 6 Reading and Writing Workbook*, colour in a circle.

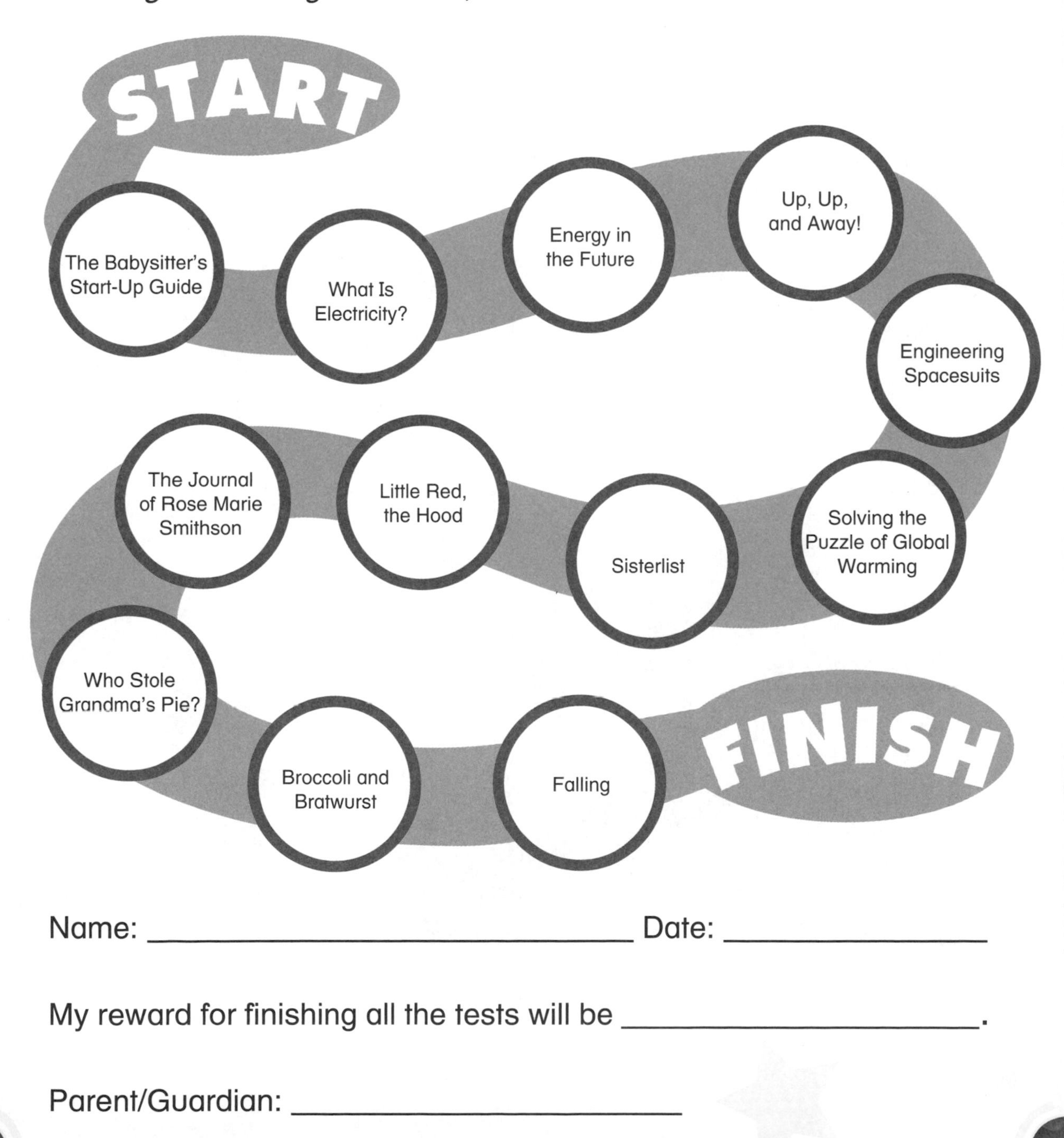

Name: ______________________________ Date: ________________

My reward for finishing all the tests will be ____________________.

Parent/Guardian: ________________________

The Babysitter's Start-Up Guide

Written by Cathy Rondina

Are you thinking about becoming a babysitter? If so, great! Babysitting can earn you a little extra money and provide an important service for people in your community. This guide is designed to help you get started.

The Job

Being a babysitter means that you are taking care of children while their parents are away. Babysitting can be fun and rewarding, but it's also a big responsibility that must be taken seriously.

Getting Ready

Before you jump into babysitting, here are a few things to consider:

Your Interests

If the idea of being alone with a couple of kids doesn't sound like fun, this probably isn't the job for you. And that's OK. But even if you enjoy being around kids, you still need to remember the following:

- Your job won't be just to hang out with the kids; you need to *look after* them.
- Kids come in all different shapes and sizes. If changing smelly diapers grosses you out, think about babysitting only older kids.

Your Family

Babysitting takes babysitters away from their own families. You need your family's permission in order to say OK to any babysitting offers.

For example, are you allowed to babysit on a school night? After midnight? When would it be OK to walk home from a babysitting job, and when should you get a ride?

Your Time

Do you really have enough time? Sit down and write a schedule of what you do every week—including schoolwork, skating lessons, soccer practice, or whatever else you're involved in. Look at your schedule and decide if you have time—and if so, when and how much time.

You might be able to sneak in a little study time while babysitting, but don't count on it!

Your Readiness

If you sometimes take care of yourself at home or you look after younger brothers or sisters, you might be ready for a babysitting job. If you haven't spent much time around younger kids, you need to get some experience first.

For example, you could volunteer to help your neighbour or family friends with their young kids. Here are some more ways to help you get ready for babysitting:

- Take a babysitting course at the local library or community centre.
- Talk to parents who hire babysitters.
- Talk to other kids who are babysitters.
- Use the Internet to read all you can about child care and first aid.

If You Think You're Ready

If you're still interested and want to give babysitting a try, then it's time to think about preparing for and getting the jobs. Take care and have fun!

Reading

1. How can this text best be described?
   - ○ a story about a difficult babysitting job
   - ○ a persuasive text about how to find the best babysitting job
   - ○ an article about being responsible
   - ● an article about how to become a babysitter

2. What does the word *Readiness* mean as used in the heading on page 9?
   - ○ creativity
   - ● preparedness and responsiblity
   - ○ punctuality
   - ○ business smarts

3. Writing a schedule of what you do every week
   - ● helps you determine your availability.
   - ○ is a great way to set up your study times.
   - ○ helps your friends set up activities.
   - ○ is required for all babysitting jobs.

4. According to this text, if you do not like changing diapers,
   - ○ you should consider a different job.
   - ○ you will learn to get used to it.
   - ● you might want to babysit older children.
   - ○ the parents will do it when they return home.

5. According to this text, you
   - ○ should never do homework while babysitting.
   - ● may have time for homework while babysitting.
   - ○ should forget about your homework.
   - ○ should babysit every night.

Writing

6. An antonym for *interested* is

- ○ excited.
- ○ enthusiastic.
- ○ sympathetic.
- ● bored.

7. In the sentence on page 9, "Here are some more ways to help you get ready for babysitting:" the colon indicates

- ○ a question.
- ● the introduction of a list.
- ○ a new page.
- ○ an unrelated story.

8. Choose the best word to complete the following sentence: "Working in a store could pay a bit more, __________ babysitting is more fun."

- ○ unless
- ● but
- ○ and
- ○ because

9. In the sentence "For example, you could volunteer to help your neighbour or family friends with their young kids," *volunteer* is used as

- ○ a noun.
- ○ an adjective.
- ○ a verb.
- ○ an adverb.

Answers are on page 112.

Reading

1. Explain how babysitting can be a fun and rewarding job. Support your answer with information from the text and your own ideas.

2. Explain why someone may not want to be a babysitter. Support your answer with information from the text and your own ideas.

Answers are on page 112.

Writing

3. Think about your own experiences either as a babysitter or as a child who has been looked after by a babysitter. Write a short story about a babysitting adventure. You can use the space below to create a graphic organizer for your story.

Answers are on page 112.

What Is Electricity?

Written by Angela Lee

Powering Our World

Electricity is a form of energy that we use daily. In fact, our world depends on it. Homes use electricity for heating, lighting, refrigerators, TVs, and every other gadget you can think of that plugs into an outlet or runs on batteries.

Can you spot at least six electrical appliances in this modern kitchen?

Today, electric lighting allows us to work or play long into the night.

Before electricity, people used oil lamps or candles for light. Because of this, they did little work after sunset.

Why do you think lighting a home with candles could be dangerous?

This engraving from the late 1800s shows the Dynamo Room in the Edison Electric Lighting Station in New York City.

Relying on Electricity

Electricity is also important outside the home.

Hospitals are full of machines that require electricity, such as heartbeat and blood-pressure monitors and lasers used for surgery.

Businesses also rely on electricity for computers, lighting, and many more machines. Office buildings need electricity to run lights, elevators, switchboards, phones, photocopiers, and air conditioners.

Schools rely on electricity too. Imagine what your school would be like without electricity!

Cellphones run on electricity stored in batteries.

How Do Machines Use Electricity?

Most machines take electrical energy and transform it into other kinds of energy. For example, TVs and computers transform electrical energy into light (which makes the images you see on the screen or monitor), heat, and sound. In a blender or drill, electrical energy is transformed into motion, sound, and heat.

Electricity also plays a role in machines that get power from other sources. A car engine runs on gasoline, but the car's battery stores electricity that is used to create the sparks that start the gasoline burning. And the car's headlights, turn signals, radio, and dashboard instruments also run on electrical energy from the battery.

How Does Electricity Travel?

Most electricity is generated in power plants. High-power transmission lines on tall towers carry electricity to substations closer to where it will be used. From the substations, electricity is carried by overhead or underground wires to homes and businesses.

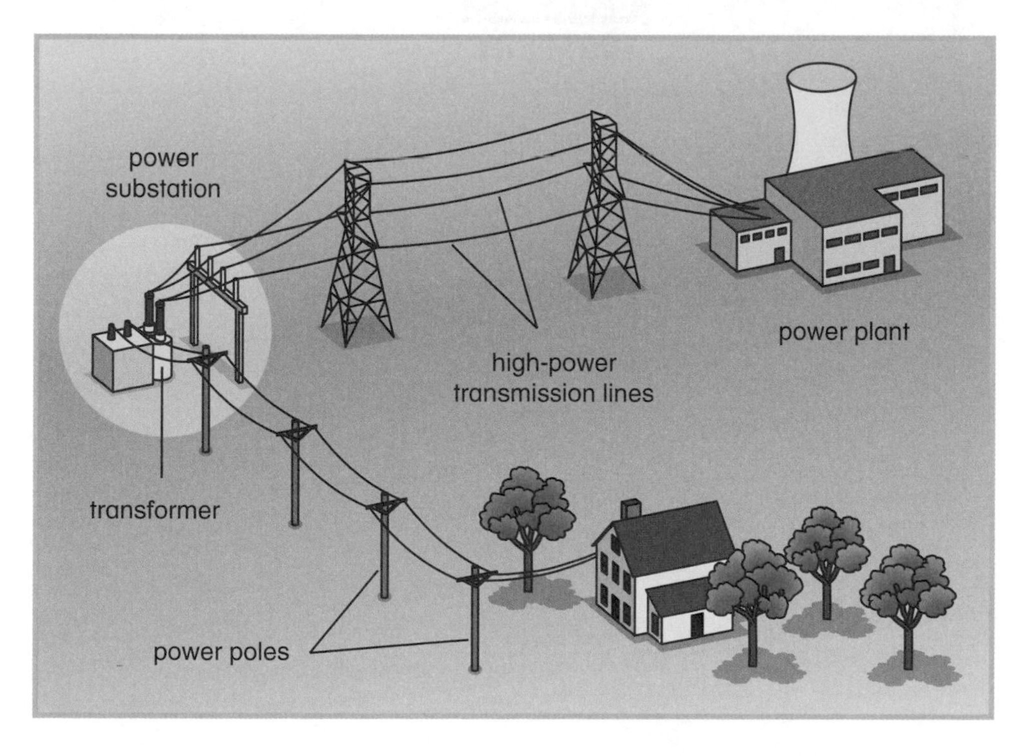

In your neighbourhood, where do you see the items shown in this diagram?

What Happens When You Flip the Switch?

Wires throughout your home provide pathways for electricity to travel to different rooms. Light switches allow us to control the electricity used for overhead lighting. When a light switch is in the "off" position, it creates a gap in the pathway, or circuit, so electricity cannot travel to the light bulb. When you flip the switch to the "on" position, the gap is closed and electricity travels to the light bulb. The power switches on many electrical devices work in the same way.

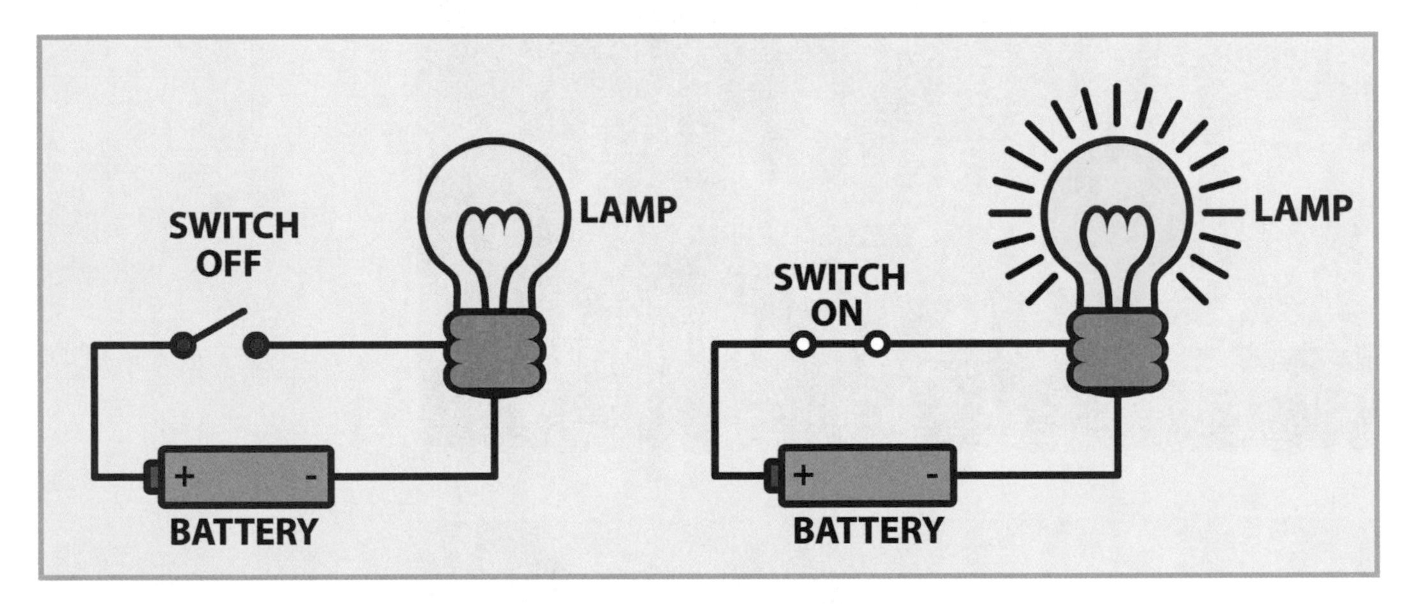

This diagram shows how a basic switch works to turn a light on and off.

Conductors and Insulators

Materials that electricity can travel through easily are called *conductors*. Wires made of solid metal are used in electrical devices because electricity can travel through metals easily. Materials that electricity does not travel through are called *insulators*. Wood, rubber, and most plastics are insulators. Many wires have a plastic covering that protects people from making contact with electricity, which can be harmful. Engineers and others who work with electricity wear rubber-soled shoes. It's very dangerous if electricity passes through the body and into the ground. Rubber soles stop this from happening.

Electrical workers keep power lines in good repair so that electricity can travel to your home. Rubber-soled shoes help protect them against electrocution if they accidentally contact electricity.

Reading

1. How can this text best be described?
   - ○ a story about electricity
   - ○ a nonfiction article about electricity
   - ○ a person's point of view on electricity
   - ○ a first-person narrative about how electricity affects the narrator's life

2. Why should people who work with electricity wear rubber-soled shoes?
   - ○ Rubber is an insulator.
   - ○ Rubber is a conductor.
   - ○ Rubber grips the ground well.
   - ○ Rubber is inexpensive.

3. According to the text, why do wires have a plastic covering?
   - ○ Plastic covers conduct electricity.
   - ○ Plastic covers are rigid and durable.
   - ○ Plastic covers prevent direct contact with electricity.
   - ○ Plastic covers come in many colours.

4. Which is the best conductor?
   - ○ metal
   - ○ rubber
   - ○ plastic
   - ○ wood

5. What does the diagram on page 18 show?
   - ○ It shows how to make electricity.
   - ○ It shows the flow of electricity from a battery, through a switch, to a light bulb.
   - ○ It shows the flow of electricity from a battery to a coffee maker.
   - ○ It shows the proper way to wire a night light.

Writing

6. A synonym for *require* is
- ○ use.
- ○ like.
- ○ want.
- ○ need.

7. In the statement "The car's battery stores electricity," the apostrophe indicates
- ○ ownership/possession.
- ○ a plural.
- ○ a contraction.
- ○ past tense.

8. Choose the sentence that correctly shows proper nouns.
- ○ This is the dynamo room in the Edison electric lighting station in New York City.
- ○ This is the Dynamo Room in the Edison Electric Lighting Station in New York City.
- ○ This is the Dynamo room in the Edison Electric Lighting station in New York city.
- ○ This is the dynamo room in the Edison Electric lighting station in New York City.

9. Choose the sentence that is written correctly.
- ○ Before electricity, people used oil lamps or candles for light and did little work after sunset.
- ○ Before electricity people used oil lamps or candles for light and did little work after sunset.
- ○ Before electricity people used oil lamps, or candles for light and did little work after sunset.
- ○ Before electricity people used oil lamps or candles for light, and did little work after sunset.

Answers are on page 112.

Reading

1. What role does electricity play in making a car run? Support your answer with information from the text. Your answer can include a diagram.

2. Why do you think power outages occur in homes when there are heavy winds? Support your answer with information from the text and your own ideas. Your answer can include a diagram.

Answers are on page 112.

Writing

3. Explain how electricity is able to reach your school.
Your answer can include a diagram.

4. Some families keep emergency kits in their homes in case there is a power outage. What do you think should be in an emergency kit? Write a detailed paragraph explaining your ideas.

Answers are on pages 112 to 113.

Energy in the Future

Written by John Williams

The world—and particularly Canada—is slowly moving away from the burning of fossil fuels for energy. Burning fossil fuels for energy releases carbon dioxide and other harmful substances into the environment.

Fossil fuels include natural gas, coal, and oil (oil is used to create the gas used in most cars). Another term for these energy sources is non-renewable, because these fuels *will* eventually run out.

How can we reduce our use of fossil fuels? One answer is renewable energy sources. Renewable energy sources use resources that will always be around, like sunlight, flowing water, and wind.

Solar Power

Do you want to know the easiest, most readily available, and inexhaustible form of energy? Just look up! The Sun provides clean energy. People who install solar panels on their homes save money on their electricity bills. The only cost is the initial installation of the solar panels.

This car is solar-powered.

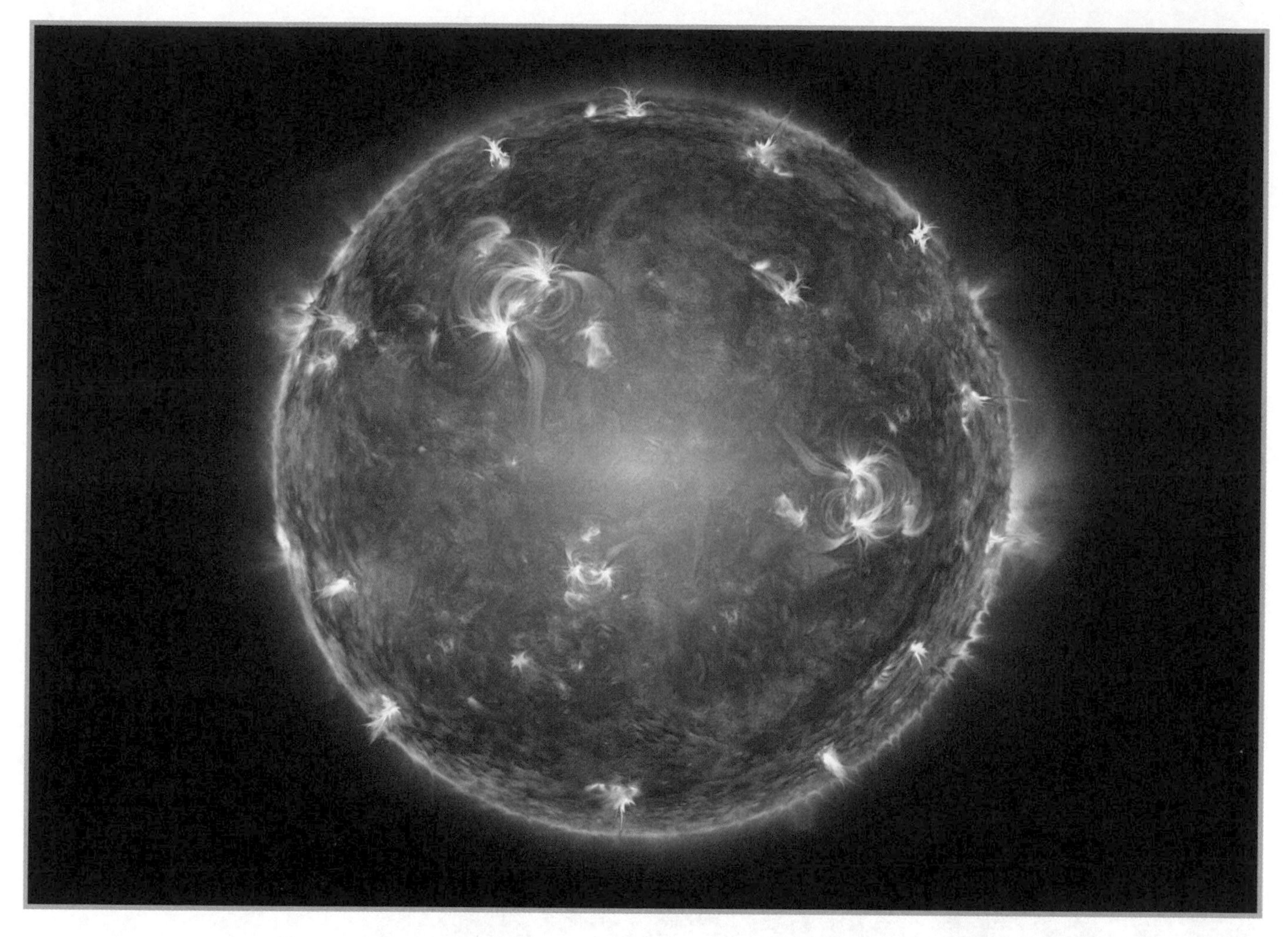

This is a close-up of the burning Sun.

Another example of harnessing the Sun's energy can be found in solar-powered lighting. In solar-powered lights, a photoelectric cell turns sunlight into electricity.

Water Power

Have you ever stood near a giant waterfall and felt the force of the water crashing down into the river below? That powerful flow creates energy that can be used as electricity. This energy is called *hydro power* or *hydroelectricity*.

Although hydro power causes less pollution than fossil fuels, hydro power is not entirely a "clean" energy source. Creating dams to harness hydroelectricity can change and damage the environment, particularly when the flow of water is cut off or redirected. Plants and animals that live near hydro dams are affected, usually adversely.

Wind Power

Wind power has been used for centuries. In the Netherlands, wooden windmills dot the landscape. In fact, 10 percent of the energy people in the Netherlands need comes from either wind or Sun. Their government plans to raise that figure to 40 percent by 2030. Of course, it helps that the Netherlands is a coastal country, with strong and steady winds. In Canada, we are slowly increasing the number of windmills we use to create energy.

This photo shows two typical sights in the Netherlands: windmills and tulips!

Hydrogen Power

We can create hydrogen gas by running electricity through water. Hydrogen power is created by burning hydrogen gas. This is one gas that burns without creating pollutants. Hydrogen power is also a lot more efficient than other sources of energy. However, hydrogen gas is extremely expensive, difficult to transport, and highly flammable.

Speeding to a New Age

For over a century, the gas we use in cars came from crude oil, which becomes petroleum when refined. These oil supplies may dwindle to nothing in the years to come, so car companies are looking at alternatives. These alternatives include both renewable fuels (made from alcohol, animal fat, or vegetable oil) and non-renewable fuels (made from coal or natural gas). Car companies are also producing electric cars—cars that just take a simple battery charge to get moving.

Did you know that many race cars use methanol, a form of alcohol?

Reading

1. Burning coal, gas, and oil
   - ● pollutes Earth's environment.
   - ○ is a form of solar energy.
   - ○ is a form of wind energy.
   - ○ does not happen in the Netherlands.

2. Solar-powered lights
   - ○ use wind power to create light.
   - ● turn the Sun's energy into electricity.
   - ○ turn electricity into sunlight.
   - ○ use animal fat to create light.

3. The Netherlands uses windmills because
   - ● the country is located on a coastline with strong and steady winds.
   - ○ they are pretty.
   - ○ wind power is not considered a clean source of energy.
   - ○ they don't get enough sunshine for solar power.

4. Researchers have come up with solutions for replacing crude oil. Which solution is suggested in the text?
   - ○ promoting the use of public transportation and carpooling
   - ○ encouraging people to walk to work and school
   - ● changing the engines in cars so they can burn alternative fuels
   - ○ creating driverless cars

Writing

5. A synonym for *efficient* is
- ○ ineffective.
- ● resourceful.
- ○ useless.
- ○ unfruitful.

6. Choose the word that is a noun.
- ○ photoelectric
- ○ only
- ● sunlight
- ○ hydroelectric

7. Choose the sentence that is written correctly.
- ○ For over a century the gas we use in cars came from crude oil or petroleum?
- ○ For over a century, the gas we use in cars, came from crude oil, or petroleum.
- ○ For over a century the gas we use in cars came from crude oil or petroleum
- ● For over a century, the gas we use in cars came from crude oil or petroleum.

8. An antonym for *steady* is
- ○ consistent.
- ○ uninterrupted.
- ● irregular.
- ○ stable.

Answers are on page 113.

Reading

1. Explain the differences between renewable and non-renewable energy sources.

2. Explain why hydro power can be good for the environment. Next, explain why hydro power can be bad for the environment.

Writing

3. Why do you think hydrogen power might be considered the "wonder fuel of the future"?

4. Why do you think it is important for scientists to continue developing alternative energy technologies?

Answers are on page 113.

Up, Up, and Away!

Written by June Loves

What Is a Hot-Air Balloon?

A hot-air balloon is a huge envelope, or bag, made of light material that is filled with heated air. Passengers are carried in a basket (also called a gondola) suspended underneath. Hot-air balloons rise because the air inside the bag is warmer and lighter than the surrounding air.

What Are the Parts of a Hot-Air Balloon?

1. The envelope is made of materials that are light but tough, such as nylon. The bigger the envelope, the more weight it can lift into the air.
2. The skirt channels hot air into the envelope.
3. One or two propane-gas burners keep the air in the envelope hot.
4. Short ropes, and sometimes wires, attach the basket to the balloon.
5. The basket is made of light, flexible wicker and holds the people, gas cylinders, and flight instruments.

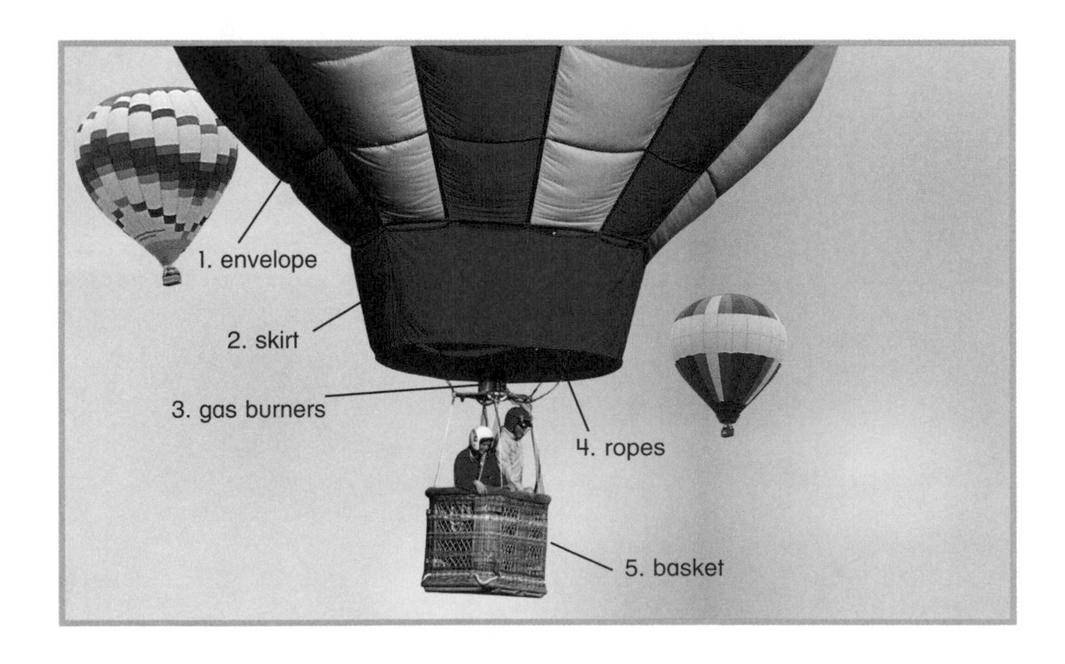

How Do Hot-Air Balloons Work?

Air that has been heated by the hot flames of a gas burner rises and collects in the balloon.

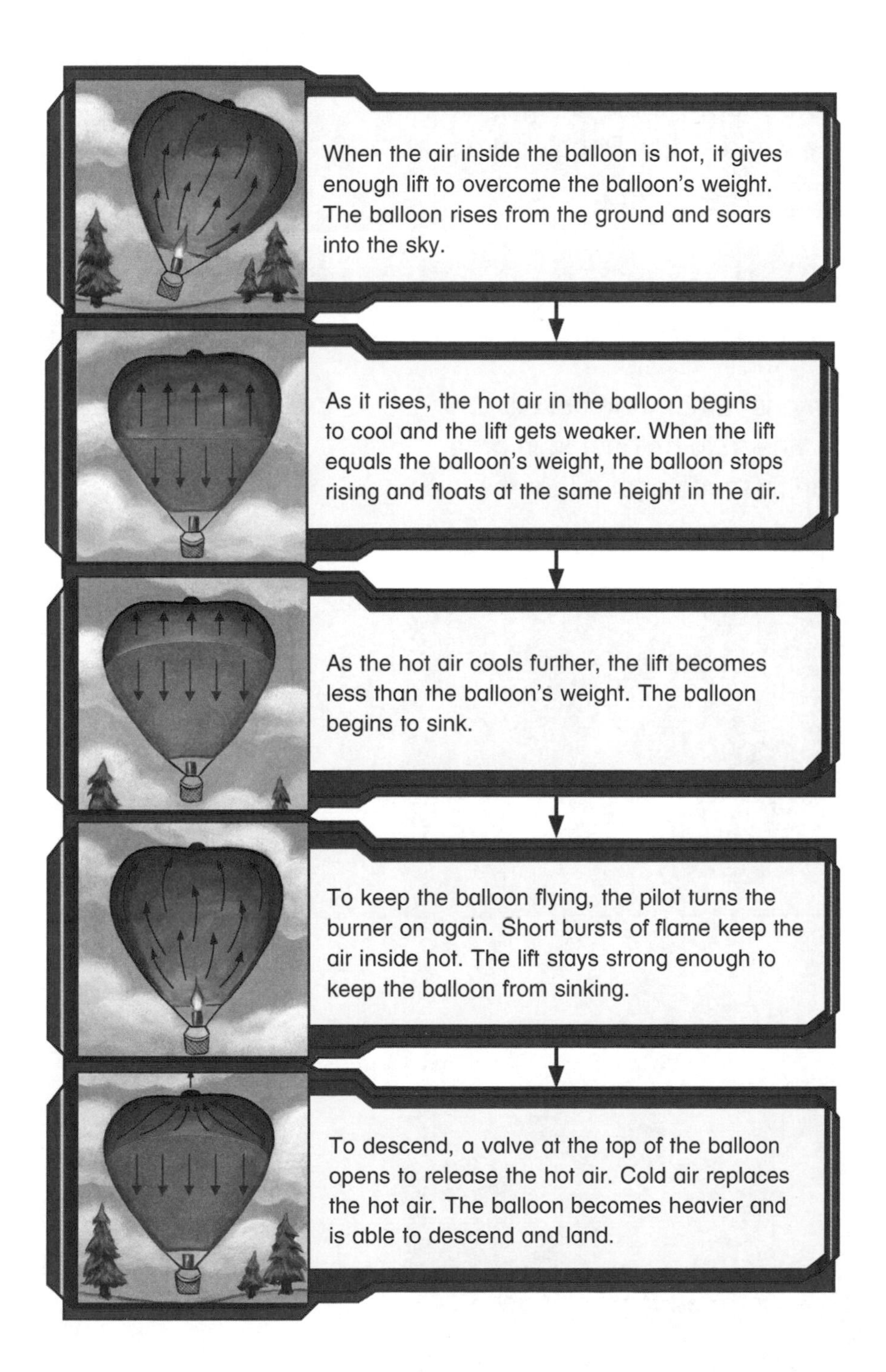

How Do People Use Hot-Air Balloons?

Modern hot-air balloons are used for leisure and sport. They are very large and can carry up to 30 people in the basket beneath the envelope. Nylon, or another light and durable material, is used for the envelope. Patterns are used to cut the material into panels and create envelopes of many different shapes. Ballooning is an exciting and popular sport all over the world today. People take part in rallies and races to break long-distance records.

What Is the Difference between a Helium Balloon and a Hot-Air Balloon?

Helium balloons are filled with helium gas rather than hot air. Helium is lighter than air and does not need to be heated in order to lift the balloon. Helium balloons can fly much higher than hot-air balloons.

These hot-air balloons are flying above a rocky landscape in Cappadocia, Turkey.

What Are Some of the Problems with Hot-Air Balloons?

- There is no control over the direction a hot-air balloon can take. The direction of the flight depends on where the wind takes the balloon. You can wait a long time for the wind to be in the right direction. You can go in the wrong direction when the wind changes.
- Bad weather conditions, such as a windstorm, can make it difficult to travel in a hot-air balloon.
- Balloons can only carry a small number of passengers.

Balloonists inflate their balloon in preparation for flight.

Reading

1. To make a hot-air balloon rise, the pilot needs to
   - ○ turn the burners on.
   - ○ rotate the skirt.
   - ○ shift the wires on the gondola.
   - ○ turn the burners off.

2. What is a gondola?
   - ○ a device used to create heat
   - ○ a device used for navigation
   - ○ a rubber cord that dangles loosely
   - ○ a container that carries passengers

3. The envelope of a hot-air balloon
   - ○ holds large amounts of helium.
   - ○ is made of a thick plastic.
   - ○ is made of tough, but light, materials.
   - ○ is made of flexible wicker.

4. Patterned panels on hot-air balloons
   - ○ are used to store helium.
   - ○ create a variety of envelopes.
   - ○ are only for decoration.
   - ○ protect the gondola from birds.

5. The diagram on page 37 shows
   - ○ how a helium balloon rises.
   - ○ how a helium balloon falls.
   - ○ how to make a hot-air balloon.
   - ○ how a hot-air balloon rises.

Writing

6. What does the word *descend* mean?

- ○ to sink
- ○ to move quickly
- ○ to rise
- ○ to move slowly

7. Choose the sentence that is written correctly.

- ○ On, clear summer mornings people enjoy going hot-air ballooning, with friends.
- ○ On clear summer mornings people enjoy, going hot-air ballooning with friends.
- ○ On clear summer, mornings people enjoy going hot-air ballooning with friends.
- ○ On clear summer mornings, people enjoy going hot-air ballooning with friends.

8. A synonym for *leisure* is

- ○ simple.
- ○ work.
- ○ effort.
- ○ recreation.

9. An antonym for *difficult* is

- ○ effortless.
- ○ tough.
- ○ demanding.
- ○ troublesome.

Answers are on page 113.

Reading

1. How can wind conditions make flying a balloon dangerous? Support your answer with information from the text and your own ideas. Your answer can include a diagram.

2. Compare and contrast helium balloons and hot-air balloons. Your answer can include a chart.

Writing

3. Imagine you have won a trip in a hot-air balloon. Write a story about your experience.

Answers are on pages 113 to 114.

Engineering a Spacesuit

Written by Helena Ng

When astronauts go into outer space, their spacesuit must provide them with everything they need to survive. Spacesuits allow astronauts to move easily so that they can complete tasks outside the spacecraft during spacewalks. It is important that spacesuits are designed appropriately to meet the needs of astronauts and their missions.

In 1965, the very first spacewalk lasted 12 minutes. Nowadays, spacewalks can last up to 8 hours! As astronauts stay outside the spacecraft for longer periods of time, they experience extreme temperature ranges. In direct sunlight, the temperature can soar to 120 °C. In the shade, the temperature can plummet to –100 °C. Astronauts outside of a spacecraft can't put on and take off a parka. They have to depend on their spacesuit to keep them safe. Engineers have designed spacesuits to ensure that astronauts are kept at a safe temperature inside their suits as they move through the different extremes during long spacewalks.

Astronauts are currently using the **E**xtravehicular **M**obility **U**nit (**EMU**), a spacesuit that has been in use since 1982. One big problem with the design of this spacesuit, however, is the gloves; the gloves are bulky enough to protect the hands, but too bulky for astronauts to use tools easily. Astronauts repairing satellites have complained of loss of feeling in their hands. Balancing protection, comfort, and flexibility is an issue that engineers are trying to solve using different materials to improve the functionality and comfort of the gloves.

This spacesuit protects astronaut Philippe Perrin as he works on the International Space Station.

A spacesuit has a lot of delicate and complicated machinery, including cameras, lights, and life-support and communication systems.

Scientists and engineers are currently working on different prototypes (early samples) of spacesuits that will help astronauts who travel to Mars. One prototype, called the Z-2 suit, is designed to provide an astronaut with more mobility than in previous spacesuit designs. As engineers improve old designs and use new technology, hopefully one day soon we will see an astronaut walk on Mars!

Activity

Sometimes, astronauts have a set amount of time to complete a task, such as repairing the spacecraft. Try this activity to understand why spacesuits need to be designed to allow astronauts to move and complete their tasks more easily.

What you need:

- at least 50 linking blocks (Lego, K*nex)
- timer
- camera
- winter gloves

What you do:

1. Build a structure with at least 50 blocks. You are using your bare hands. Time how long it takes to build this structure.
2. Take a photo of your structure so that you can rebuild it.
3. Take apart the structure.
4. Put on the winter gloves. These winter gloves represent the gloves in a spacesuit. Time yourself as you use the same pieces to rebuild your structure.

Was it harder to build a structure with your bare hands or while wearing winter gloves? If it was harder, what made it more difficult?

Reading

1. According to this text,

- ○ without oxygen, your organs will contract.
- ○ without oxygen, a person will lose consciousness.
- ○ there is plenty of oxygen in space.
- ○ astronauts need spacesuits because of extreme temperatures.

2. What materials are needed for the activity?

- ○ oven mitts, blocks, timers
- ○ paper and pens
- ○ timer, blocks, camera, and winter gloves
- ○ mitts and coins

3. What have astronauts complained of when wearing gloves?

- ○ blisters
- ○ loss of feeling in their hands
- ○ their hands were too cold
- ○ the gloves didn't fit

4. Where is the Z-2 suit designed to be used?

- ○ on Earth
- ○ on the Moon
- ○ on Mars
- ○ in a spacecraft

5. In the activity, the winter gloves represent

- ○ the tools an astronaut uses on a spacewalk.
- ○ the gloves of a spacesuit.
- ○ the joints in the spacesuit arm.
- ○ the boots of the spacesuit.

Writing

6. In the third sentence on page 44, the word *appropriately* could be replaced with

- ◯ fashionably.
- ◯ lavishly.
- ◯ correctly.
- ◯ warmly.

7. Which sentence does **not** belong in the following paragraph?
(1) In 1965, the very first spacewalk lasted 12 minutes.
(2) Stars are made of gas and dust. (3) The first spacewalk was performed by Alexey Leonov. (4) Leonov's spacesuit inflated so much he couldn't use the camera on his chest.

- ◯ 1
- ◯ 2
- ◯ 3
- ◯ 4

8. Choose the best order for the following sentences:
(1) Spacesuits haven't always been this way. (2) The EMUs worn by astronauts are reusable; they can be used multiple times. (3) This means that the spacesuit would only fit the astronaut for whom it was created. (4) Originally, all spacesuits were customized.

- ◯ 2, 1, 4, 3
- ◯ 1, 4, 2, 3
- ◯ 4, 3, 1, 2
- ◯ 3, 2, 1, 4

9. In the sentence "Scientists and engineers are currently working on different prototypes (early samples) of spacesuits that will help astronauts who travel to Mars." the parentheses are used to

- ◯ enclose a definition for the word *prototypes*.
- ◯ break up the text in the sentence.
- ◯ enclose a joke.
- ◯ enclose a definition for the phrase *currently working*.

Answers are on page 114.

Reading

1. What problem in the EMU design are engineers working on? How are they solving this problem?

2. Why do you think an activity is included in this text?

Writing

3. Why did engineers have to consider temperature when designing the EMU?

4. You have been asked to join a space mission. Tomorrow, you will be boarding a spacecraft and departing on your trip. Write a journal entry about how you feel the night before the mission.

Answers are on page 114.

Solving the Puzzle of Global Warming

Written by Maisie Park

Biologist Dr. Ian Stirling has been studying polar bears in the Arctic for 35 years. About 20 years ago, he began to notice that the bears were thinner and sicker than in previous years and that there were fewer cubs. The polar bears were in trouble—but why? Dr. Stirling knew that polar bears eat ring seals *only* out on the ice, mainly from May to early July. He also knew that the ice was breaking up earlier than it had in the past. Dr. Stirling began keeping records and comparing ice breakup times with the condition of the polar bears. He found his answer. Generally, the earlier the ice broke up, the less time bears had to hunt for ring seals. Less food for the bears led to health problems and the birth of fewer cubs.

But this answer raised a new question: Why was the ice breaking up earlier?

Polar bears only hunt ring seals before the ice breaks up. Besides ice forming later and breaking up earlier, we now know that another contributor to the declining polar bear population is that there is less sea ice from year to year.

Global warming isn't new. Temperatures on Earth have varied many times during our planet's long history. Periods of cold, with ice covering much of the planet, have been followed by periods of warmth. These cycles of warm and cold can last for millions of years. Maybe the changes scientists were noticing in the polar regions were just the effects of the beginning of a new warming period. One thing we do know is that Earth's surface temperature has averaged about 15 °C for thousands of years.

Greenhouse Gases at Work

Greenhouse gases trap heat in Earth's atmosphere. Without these gases, Earth would be a chilly –19 °C. But increasing levels of greenhouse gases trap more heat, raising the temperature of the planet.

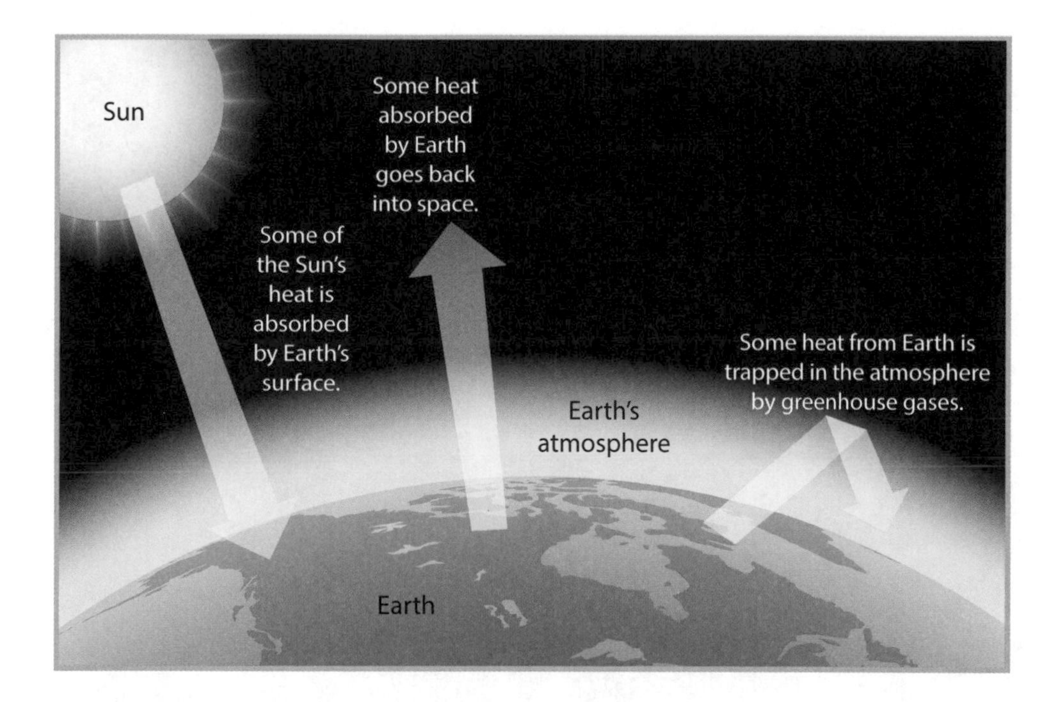

Global warming is causing some of the following:

- Plants and animals that commonly live in southern regions are living and breeding in northern regions.
- Hurricane activity is more intense, with stronger winds and more rainfall.
- Mountain glaciers and polar ice caps are melting.

In 1958, researcher Charles Keeling began measuring carbon dioxide in the atmosphere. Carbon dioxide is a gas that we breathe out. It is also released when we burn forests or fossil fuels such as oil, gas, and coal. It is one of the most important greenhouse gases. Keeling's measurements show that the amount of carbon dioxide in the atmosphere has been rising steadily each decade. Why? Since the early 1900s, fuel-burning industries have been increasing in size and number.

Vast areas of forest have been cleared, and huge amounts of polluting gases have been pumped into the atmosphere.

As more evidence was gathered, the majority of scientists came to agree that human activities are responsible for the rising levels of greenhouse gases, and that these gases are causing global warming.

There are two really good reasons to not burn forests: (1) Trees absorb carbon dioxide, so a living tree reduces carbon dioxide in the atmosphere. (2) When trees burn, the carbon dioxide stored in the trees is released.

How Can You Be Part of the Solution?

Reducing the amount of energy you use is a good starting point, since most greenhouse gas emissions come from generating and consuming energy.

- Buy less stuff. It takes energy to make and transport products.
- If you must buy something new, buy things that come with as little packaging as possible. It takes energy to make packaging.
- Recycle cans, paper, plastics—whatever your community will accept.
- Wash and reuse glass jars and some kinds of plastic containers.
- Turn off lights when you're not in a room.
- Whenever possible, walk, bike, or take the bus rather than asking for a lift.
- Take short showers rather than long baths.

If your community does not have a recycling program, you can still recycle materials at a nearby transfer station or recycling depot.

Reading

1. According to this text,

- ○ without greenhouse gases, Earth would be very cold.
- ○ polar bears hunt seals in 15 °C weather.
- ○ greenhouse gases are making Earth colder.
- ○ all the heat absorbed by Earth goes into space.

2. The majority of scientists came to agree that

- ○ rising greenhouse gases are caused by polar bears.
- ○ rising greenhouse gases are from natural causes.
- ○ rising greenhouse gases are caused by humans.
- ○ rising greenhouse gases are caused by growing forests.

3. A symptom of global warming is that

- ○ more forest areas are being cleared.
- ○ polar bears are thriving.
- ○ hurricane activity is intensifying.
- ○ more fuel is being used by cars.

4. Carbon dioxide is

- ○ a gas that we inhale.
- ○ released by the use of fossil fuels.
- ○ found only in outer space.
- ○ the gas Charles Keeling discovered.

5. The text suggests that we can be part of the solution by

- ○ washing dishes in cold water.
- ○ turning on air conditioners in winter.
- ○ buying less stuff.
- ○ having a garage sale.

Writing

6. Choose the sentence that does not belong in the following paragraph:
(1) The temperature of Earth continues to rise every year.
(2) Many scientists believe this is due to human activity.
(3) Being a scientist requires many years of study.
(4) Human behaviour has led to the rise of greenhouse gases.

- ○ 1
- ○ 2
- ○ 3
- ○ 4

7. Choose the sentence that is written correctly.

- ○ Our school has many electrical devices; phones, computers, televisions, and fans.
- ○ Our school has many electrical devices: phones, computers, televisions, and fans.
- ○ Our school has many electrical devices; phones; computers; televisions; and fans.
- ○ Our school has many electrical devices phones computers televisions and fans.

8. A synonym for *reducing* is

- ○ adding.
- ○ decreasing.
- ○ increasing.
- ○ enlarging.

9. An antonym for *warming* is

- ○ cooling.
- ○ heating.
- ○ thawing.
- ○ melting.

Answers are on page 114.

Reading

1. How is global warming affecting polar bears?

2. How does the greenhouse gases diagram on page 53 help the reader?

Writing

3. What can you do to help solve global warming? Support your answer with information from the text and your own ideas.

4. Your teacher wants to invite an environmental scientist to speak to your class about global warming. Write a detailed letter to the scientist. Explain why they should visit your class.

Answers are on pages 114 to 115.

Sisterlist

Poem written by Rowena Sommerville
Illustrated by Helen Flook

My big sister says she loves me,
says she'll take me 'round the town,
Mum says, "Ooh, you are a brick,
you never let your old ma down.
Now I won't be long, I promise,
get yourselves some fries to eat,"
gives my sister something extra,
"that's 'cause you deserve a treat,
and I know that I can trust you, be
good girls and please don't fight."
As she closed the door, my sister
pointed at me and said,
"RIGHT—

don't imagine that I like you,
I'm just giving Mum a hand,
I can't go if I don't take you,
and I need the money and
don't you walk too close behind me,
don't wear knee socks or a hat,
please don't pose or pick your nose,
and don't you look at me like that,
don't ask me to go in toy shops,
you can see I'm much too hip,
don't wear clothes that look as though
you'd worn them on a camping trip,
if we see some tasty boys,
then please attempt some sort of cool,
and don't embarrass me by smirking
if we meet some kids from school,
and don't go touching things in the store,
don't you wear that gruesome coat,
and when I'm chatting with my friends
don't cough, or hum, or clear your throat,

and don't start whining that you're bored,
or moaning that you've had enough,
and don't tell me you've got a blister,
learn to bear it, life is tough,
don't go pulling funny faces,
don't go asking me for money,
and if you're spoken to, act normal,
don't talk common, don't talk funny,
and don't butt in on conversations,
don't ear-hole the things we say,
if some nice boy chats me up,
then have the sense to walk away,
don't go asking me for ice cream,
DON'T act like a little kid,
don't go telling tales at home,
and don't blame me for what YOU did,
and don't tell Mum I'm wearing lipstick,
no one likes a dirty sneak,
and if you give me any grief
I'll beat you up at school next week."

Well, all of this went on for ages,
then we heard the backdoor key,
Mum came in, and said, “Back so soon, girls?
Who’ll make me a cup of tea?
Are you two behaving well?
Was that a quarrel that I heard?”
and then I looked at my big sister,
but I didn’t say a word.

Reading

1. What does the word *quarrel* on page 63 mean?
   - ○ argument
   - ○ agreement
   - ○ settlement
   - ○ description

2. Choose the pair of words that completes the following sentence correctly: "At first my sister spoke ____, but afterwards she _____ mean."
   - ○ nicely, becoming
   - ○ nicely, became
   - ○ nicer, become
   - ○ nice, become

3. Why is this selection called a poem?
   - ○ because it has a rhythm and some of the lines rhyme
   - ○ because the lines are short
   - ○ because the characters and plot are made up
   - ○ because it uses dialogue

4. In the line "learn to bear it, life is tough" on page 62, the word *bear* means
   - ○ an animal in the woods.
   - ○ to endure something difficult.
   - ○ to confess something.
   - ○ to be empty.

5. Which of the following is one of the rules the older sister gives her younger sister?
   - ○ DON'T act like a little kid.
   - ○ Talk to her friends.
   - ○ Ask her for money.
   - ○ Don't wear a sweater.

Writing

6. The word *Mum* is capitalized because
- ○ it is a common noun.
- ○ it is a pronoun.
- ○ it is a proper noun.
- ○ it is an adjective.

7. A synonym for *embarrass* is
- ○ calm.
- ○ aid.
- ○ explain.
- ○ shame.

8. Choose the verb.
- ○ lipstick
- ○ gruesome
- ○ funny
- ○ deserve

9. Choose the sentence that is correct.
- ○ "Don't start wining that you are bored."
- ○ "Dont start whining that you are board."
- ○ "Don't start whining that you are bored."
- ○ "Don't start whining that you our bored."

10. *That's* is a contraction for
- ○ That was.
- ○ That is.
- ○ That were.
- ○ That are.

Answers are on page 115.

Reading

1. Why does the mother describe the older sister as a *brick*?

2. How does the older sister's attitude change when the mother is not around?

Writing

3. The older sister has a lot to say to the younger sister. If the younger sister, the narrator, were to write a verse about how she feels, what would she say? You can write a list, a poem, or a paragraph in response.

Answers are on page 115.

Little Red, the Hood

Written by Peg Kehret
Illustrated by Matt Roussel

Just because I'm a wolf, everyone assumes I'm the bad guy. People say, "Poor Little Red Riding Hood. Poor old Grannie."

Ha! If the truth were known, Little Red and Grannie would be arrested for fraud and intent to deceive a police officer. These two women are real con artists, but Little Red's cute, and can scream hysterically, so everyone believed her version of what happened. Nobody would listen to me. Well, I think it's time the real story got told. I'm tired of taking the rap.

It began late one Sunday afternoon, deep in the woods. Now, I live in the woods, you understand. These are *my woods*—well, mine and the bank's. I have another 14 years to go on my mortgage. The point is, the woods are my home and Little Red was trespassing. Naturally, when I saw her running across my property, I stopped her and asked her what she was doing.

You probably think she told me she was on her way to visit her sick grandmother. Wrong. She told me that the most incredible thing had just happened.

She said, "I was walking through the woods, looking for wildflowers, when I spotted something hidden under a bush. Being curious, I looked closer and was astonished to find several stacks of thousand-dollar bills. Since there was no one around to claim the money, I put it in my basket and now I'm on my way to my sick grannie's house to call the police." She lifted one corner of the napkin that covered her basket and gave me a quick peek. There were bundles of cash, neatly bound with rubber bands. A little prickle of excitement ran down my back, clear to the tip of my tail.

"Are you sure you want to call the police?" I asked her. "They'll confiscate the money and probably never find the owner. Think what you could do with all that cash."

She looked at me and blinked her big blue eyes innocently. "Oh, I can't keep it," she said. "I'd be too nervous to spend thousand-dollar bills. I usually only have tens and twenties."

Then she said, "It's too bad it's Sunday and the banks are closed, because otherwise I'd be willing to trade you all this money for whatever you have in smaller bills."

Now, that statement made my fur stand on end. I didn't know how much cash she had in the basket, but I'd glimpsed a lot of little bundles. I told her it didn't matter if it was Sunday. I had a bank card for the cash machine. I offered to draw out everything in my account, all two thousand dollars, and we'd trade. Then she gave me that innocent smile and said she wouldn't be at all afraid to spend two thousand in tens and twenties.

By then, my heart was pounding. I had visions of myself driving around the woods in my new Rolls Royce.

Little Red and I hurried to the First Interforest Bank. I got out my little plastic card and punched the numbers into the machine. As the tens and twenties came out, I handed them to Red and she tucked them in her pocket. It took a while, but eventually my account was empty and Red's pocket was bulging. She handed me the basket and suggested I wait until I got home to open it, in case anyone dishonest was watching. Then we shook hands and went our separate ways.

I took the shortcut back to the woods, locked my lair, and opened the basket. It was quite a shock. There were lots of bundles, but they weren't thousand-dollar bills. They were papers, cut in the size of bills. The only stack that had a real bill on top was the one in the corner, and that bill was one hundred dollars, not one thousand. I was furious. I'd been bilked out of my life savings!

I rushed to Grannie's house and went inside. The bed was empty; Grannie, apparently, had had a miraculous recovery. I quickly put on Grannie's nightgown and nightcap and climbed into bed to wait for Little Red.

You know the rest of the story. Red showed up with an undercover agent disguised as a woodchopper. Grannie jumped out of the closet, and the two of them concocted that terrible story about me. Before I could protest, I was handcuffed and on my way to the slammer.

And do you know the worst part of all? The part that never made it into the storybooks? First Interforest Bank hit me with thirty-two dollars in service charges for overdrawing my account.

Reading

1. Why does the wolf stop Little Red when he first sees her?
   - ○ to steal her money
   - ○ because she has a basket of food
   - ○ because she is trespassing
   - ○ because he wants to eat her

2. What does Little Red claim she is looking for in the woods?
   - ○ money
   - ○ her grandmother
   - ○ wildflowers
   - ○ the wolf

3. In the statement "Are you sure you want to call the police? They'll confiscate the money," *they'll* refers to
   - ○ the bankers.
   - ○ the police.
   - ○ the woodsmen.
   - ○ the person who lost the money.

4. The woodchopper is really
   - ○ a traffic cop.
   - ○ an undercover agent.
   - ○ a bank guard.
   - ○ a wildlife officer.

5. How has the writer played with the traditional story of "Little Red Riding Hood"?
   - ○ by telling the story from the perspective of the wolf
   - ○ by setting the story in a more modern time
   - ○ by making Little Red Riding Hood and Grannie the "bad" characters
   - ○ all of the above

Writing

6. In the line "I'd been bilked out of my life's savings!" on page 70, *bilked* means

- ◯ to be given something.
- ◯ to be cheated.
- ◯ to receive an award.
- ◯ to be compensated.

7. A synonym for *fraud* is

- ◯ scam.
- ◯ truth.
- ◯ honesty.
- ◯ intelligence.

8. Choose the words that complete the following sentence correctly: "Little Red ______ the money while _______ in the woods."

- ◯ discover, walk
- ◯ discovering, walking
- ◯ discovered, walking
- ◯ discovered, walk

9. Choose the adverb.

- ◯ nightgown
- ◯ innocently
- ◯ pocket
- ◯ corner

10. In the line "the two of them concocted that terrible story" on page 71, *concocted* means

- ◯ lied.
- ◯ told.
- ◯ made up.
- ◯ remembered.

Answers are on page 115.

Reading

1. How is Little Red able to convince the wolf that she is trustworthy?

2. How does the reader know that the wolf is full of excitement during his meeting with Little Red?

Writing

3. What would you do if you discovered a basket full of thousand-dollar bills? Write a paragraph explaining your ideas.

Answers are on page 115.

The Journal of Rose Marie Smithson

Historical Fiction written by Laura Morgan

November 6, 1833

Father let me help him in the smithy three days this week. He says to Mother that it is not fair that she has four daughters to help her when he has no sons to learn his trade. And when I was working the bellows today, a gentleman who was having his horse shod called me "boy" and asked me to fetch him some water! I was wearing an extra apron of Father's and a cap, so I can understand his mistake. Matilda says that she would be mortified, but I think it is rather funny.

April 9, 1834

I was surprised to come across this journal on the bookshelf. It has been so long since I have written. I am so tall. I am taller even than Mother; I reach up to Father's nose. I like to help in the smithy, and Father says I am becoming quite skilled—it's too bad I'm not a boy because I could be his apprentice.

January 27, 1835

I am so afraid and cannot share my fears with anyone. Mother looks worried all the time, and I don't want to frighten my little sisters. Father is sick and getting worse. I fear he may have cholera. This winter is terrible cold, and with Father unable to work, we are running short of food.

March 15, 1835

I am strong and red from helping in the smithy. Although Mother doesn't know it, I seldom wear my corset—it is so tight. I have to wear Father's old boots; we have no money for new shoes, and my feet have grown so. Father lets me wear trousers in the smithy as my skirt gets soiled.

October 11, 1835

Father has been very tired the past few weeks. We don't tell Mother, but he sits on his stool by the fire and directs me to do the work. I wish his health would improve.

December 27, 1835

I am numb. I have no one to turn to. Father is dead. Wonderful, warm, laughing Father. How can he be gone? What are we to do?

February 25, 1836

Today, when I brought Matilda her dinner at the seamstress shop, I wore Father's trousers and my old cap. I felt free and invisible in my disguise. The seamstress called to Matilda, "Your brother is here." Matilda stared and covered her giggle with a dainty hand, and winked just as Father used to.

April 23, 1836

I have made a friend. His name is Thomas and he thinks I am a boy. Thomas likes to talk a lot, and it doesn't seem to bother him that I don't say much. I would like to speak more often but am afraid my voice would give me away. I am unhappy about deceiving him, but to confess now would embarrass us both.

May 17, 1836

There is talk around town of a railway! Imagine—the first railway in Lower Canada, starting here in La Prairie! The cousins in Boston wrote once about the great locomotives and the tracks that stretch for hundreds of miles! Thomas says they will need a gang of strong boys and men to lay the tracks. The pay will be good, and if I am hired on, Mother will not have to ask for help from her Boston relatives.

La Prairie

May 25, 1836

We start working on the railway tomorrow, at daybreak! Matilda is worried that they will find me out, but I have wrestled Thomas and although he beat my right arm, I beat his left. If he is strong enough, I am strong enough. It will be sweaty work, though, and I must be careful or I will give myself away!

May 26, 1836

My arms are trembling, but I must write a little. We worked from sunup to sundown. When we arrived, the crew master sent some fellows to lay the ties and tracks, but Thomas and me and some others he set opposite each other, ready to drive the spikes. He had me drive the first spike, with the others watching. The sledge was heavy, and the spikes were very solid. The blow landed with a sharp, ringing tone that brought suddenly to my mind the image of Father shaping a horseshoe.

Reading

1. What does the word *trade* mean as used in the first journal entry on page 76?
   - ○ exchange
   - ○ deal
   - ○ transaction
   - ○ job

2. The entry for April 9, 1834, is primarily about
   - ○ Rose Marie's growth and blacksmithing ability.
   - ○ the family's financial difficulties.
   - ○ Rose Marie's clothing.
   - ○ Father's illness.

3. Cholera is
   - ○ a type of metal.
   - ○ an illness.
   - ○ a type of tool.
   - ○ an item made in a smithy.

4. Why doesn't Rose Marie talk a lot when she is with Thomas?
   - ○ Rose Marie is shy.
   - ○ Rose Marie is grieving over her father's death.
   - ○ Rose Marie fears her high voice will give away her secret.
   - ○ Rose Marie is insecure about her blacksmithing abilities.

5. Where is this historical fiction set?
   - ○ in the 1860s, in La Prairie, Upper Canada
   - ○ in the 1730s, in La Payez, Lower Canada
   - ○ in the 1830s, in Last Prayers, Lower Canada
   - ○ in the 1830s, in La Prairie, Lower Canada

Writing

6. The semicolon in the passage "I have to wear Father's old boots; we have no money for new shoes, and my feet have grown so" indicates
   - ○ a list of items.
   - ○ a specific time.
   - ○ multiple statements that share a close connection.
   - ○ a new topic.

7. In the phrase "the great locomotives," *great* is
   - ○ a noun.
   - ○ an adjective.
   - ○ an adverb.
   - ○ a proper noun.

8. Choose the best words to complete the following sentence: "It will be sweaty work, ______, and I must be careful _____ I will give myself away!"
   - ○ though, or
   - ○ although, so
   - ○ and, unless
   - ○ so, while

9. A synonym for *numb* is
   - ○ shocked.
   - ○ compassionate.
   - ○ sensitive.
   - ○ responsive.

Answers are on page 116.

Reading

1. Historical fiction combines real events and fictional storylines and characters. What characteristics of historical fiction does this text use?

2. Explain why the third, fourth, and fifth journal entries are effective in creating a sense of distress for the reader. Support your answer with specific details from the text.

Writing

3. What do you think might happen if the other railway workers discover that Rose Marie is a girl?

4. Imagine you are Rose Marie. Write your next two journal entries.

Answers are on page 116.

Who Stole Grandma's Pie?

Mystery Story written by Myra Sanderman

My grandma is the best pie-maker in the world. So when she called me—the best detective she knows—to say that one of her pies was missing, I knew that it was serious.

I hurried to Grandma's house to look for clues. The kitchen was still warm from the oven. The air smelled buttery and sweet. When I hugged Grandma hello, I realized that I hadn't visited her in a long time.

"Start from the beginning," I said. I pulled a stool over to the sink, where Grandma was washing dishes.

"I cut the pie into six pieces," she began, "in this pie plate." She showed me the plate. There were only a few crumbs left.

"The pie is definitely missing," I said, scooping up the crumbs and popping them into my mouth.

Grandma sniffed. "Sammy, it was pumpkin."

"A *pumpkin* pie!" I shouted, nearly jumping off the stool. "My favourite kind. This is even more serious than I thought."

I took a small notebook and pencil from my pocket. "Now, when did you last see this pie?"

"You mean the whole pie?" she asked.

The question surprised me, but I just nodded. "I baked it this morning," said Grandma. "Then the doorbell rang. It was that nice young man who rakes my leaves."

"Just as I suspected," I said, writing down "leaf raker" in my notebook. "He stole the pie."

“Oh, dear, no,” Grandma said. “He just wanted me to know that he was finished. He did such a good job that I gave him a piece of pie.”

I put a line through “leaf raker” and started a new page. “Then what happened, Grandma?”

Grandma squirted more soap into the sink as she thought about my question.

“When I went outside with the young man’s piece of pie, the mail carrier was there. She told me she could smell that pie all the way from the curb.”

“Aha!” I said, writing “mail carrier” in my notebook. “While you were busy with the leaf raker, the mail carrier sneaked into the house and stole the pie. Just as I suspected.” I felt pretty good about that bit of detective work.

Grandma shook her head. “No, I gave her a piece of pie myself. She didn’t have to steal it.”

“Go on,” I said, getting a little concerned about having to cross out another suspect.

"Then the phone rang, and it was my neighbour, Gloria Ketchum. You know, the woman with the cats?"

I nodded and wrote "G.K." in my book.

"She is such a dear. Calls me every day to see if I need anything. So I invited her over for some pie and tea with me. Her daughter came, too."

"Grandma!" I said. "No one stole the pie. It's missing because you gave away all the pieces."

Grandma looked thoughtful.

I held up my hand to show her on my fingers. "One piece to the leaf raker. Another piece to the mail carrier is two. You and Mrs. Ketchum each had a piece. That's two more, which makes four. And her daughter's piece is five."

"There were six pieces," Grandma reminded me.

"Hmmm," I said. "Did anyone else come to the door?"

"No," she said.

"Any more phone calls?"

She shook her head.

I scratched mine. This *was* a mystery.

"Maybe it was one of Mrs. Ketchum's cats," I said. "Did you find any paw prints in the flour?"

Grandma giggled.

I had to search for more clues.

I opened the refrigerator. Grandma keeps everything in her fridge: crackers, chips, bread, cookies. She says that things stay fresher that way.

"What about *this* piece of pie?" I asked, opening a container.

Grandma looked surprised. "Now where did that come from?"

"I found it on the middle shelf," I said.

"Isn't that something?" she said, taking the piece from me. It was a big one. "That's it, all right."

Grandma put it in the pie plate and stuck it in the oven. "I'll just warm it up a bit. You must be hungry from all that detective work."

While the pie was warming, I thought about the case. I think the real mystery was whether Grandma had said that the pie was missing just so I'd come over for a visit.

When I asked her about that, she gave me a kiss and said I was the world's greatest detective.

Which I am. I *did* find the pie. And it was delicious, just as I suspected.

Reading

1. What kind of pie does Grandma make?
   - ○ pecan
   - ○ apple
   - ○ pumpkin
   - ○ blueberry

2. This selection is
   - ○ a mystery story.
   - ○ historical nonfiction.
   - ○ a biography.
   - ○ a procedural text.

3. Where does Sammy find the missing piece?
   - ○ in the oven
   - ○ in the mailbox
   - ○ with the cats
   - ○ in the fridge

4. In the sentence "What about *this* piece of pie?" on page 87, italics are used
   - ○ to indicate a question.
   - ○ to show the person is whispering.
   - ○ to emphasize the word.
   - ○ because the word is a pronoun.

5. Who is the main character in this story?
   - ○ the cat
   - ○ the leaf raker
   - ○ Sammy
   - ○ Grandma

Writing

6. Choose the words that correctly complete this sentence:
"_______ time to give the cat ____ food."

- ○ Its, its
- ○ It's, its
- ○ Its, it's
- ○ It's, it's

7. In the sentence "Grandma squirted more soap into the sink as she thought about my question," *squirted* is

- ○ an adjective.
- ○ a noun.
- ○ a verb.
- ○ an adverb.

8. A synonym for *concerned* is

- ○ troubled.
- ○ happy.
- ○ cool.
- ○ peaceful.

9. Choose the superlative adjective.

- ○ pie
- ○ mystery
- ○ said
- ○ greatest

Answers are on page 116.

Reading

1. By the end of the story, why does Sammy think Grandma claimed the pie went missing?

2. How does Sammy know that Gloria Ketchum and her daughter aren't suspects?

Writing

3. Write a story about a time that you lost something of value.

Answers are on page 116.

Broccoli and Bratwurst

Short Story written by Philippe Levesque

It was the test of times; it was the wurst of times. Bratwurst that is.

I was a contestant on a TV show: *Junior Cooking Champs.*

We had just been given our final test—to cook bratwurst over a campfire. Bratwurst is a type of sausage. A pork sausage. And I'm a vegetarian.

I had made it to the final top two cooks. I had dazzled the judges with my meatless dishes. My signature dishes are a tasty tofu stir-fry and a berry bean bombe (a bombe is a dessert made with cake and fruit—I replace the eggs, milk, and butter usually found in cakes with cashews and white beans).

So, as I looked in dismay at our ingredients, my fellow finalist grinned with delight.

Crandon the Carnivore I called him. Crandon had also wowed the judges … with his meat dishes. His multi-meat meatloaf, his ostrich triple burger, and his bacon berry donut deluxe had them all drooling.

Crandon turned his grin on me and crowed, "I guess, Virginia, for you, this competition couldn't get any wurst!" And after that awful pun, as if I was so stupid I didn't get it, he paused to ask, "Get it?"

"Yes, Crandon. Very clever!" I said flatly. Crandon was one year younger than me—11. And he reminded me of my more annoying little cousins.

Crandon also excelled at cooking over campfires. Was I doomed?

And why a campfire? Probably because a kids' camping show came on right after our show and the biggest advertiser for both shows made marshmallows. I started my campfire while I thought about my problem. I would need the fire to burn down a bit anyway.

Crandon also had his campfire going and his first sausage cooking. While I was still wondering what to use, if not the meat provided, to make my bratwurst.

I looked again at ALL the ingredients we had. Because, with the bratwurst, we were also supposed to make a broccoli salad or a purple cabbage coleslaw.

So, I had beans, lentils, nuts, vegetables, bread crumbs, and spices. And rice. Rice was good. Sticky rice would hold the other ingredients together.

But I had only an hour to get everything done!

I whirled into action—getting the rice and beans cooking, chopping up vegetables, running bread crumbs through the food processor, and then adding the other cooked ingredients. I was a tornado, tearing through everything I had to get done.

Finally, everything was mixed together. I added garlic and chilies to make the sausage extra-flavourful and spicy. My bean broccoli bratwurst was ready to go!

Now, I just had to cook them. Luckily, I'm a scout with two badges for fires—making them *and* cooking over them! My campfire was now a perfect bed of coals. I carefully set my cast-iron frying pan on top.

I glanced over to see how Crandon was doing. His method of using a stick over open flames was disastrous. There were more sausages in the fire than on the plate for the judges. And I could tell he wasn't even thinking about his coleslaw yet—I had made mine while I was waiting for the beans and rice to cook.

And, of course, the lovely thing about vegetarian sausages, they don't need a lot of time to cook. I had ten minutes left, but that was loads of time. In minutes, my sausages were a lovely brown colour.

Crandon was crying over his coleslaw. What a baby! Maybe it was the onions he was chopping. Or maybe it was the mess he had made of his plate. My plate looked beautiful! If I did say so myself.

The judges certainly thought so as they called up the winner of the whole competition: Virginia the Vegetarian!

Reading

1. What problem does Virginia have?
   - ○ She doesn't know how to cook.
   - ○ She is a very good cook, but she wasn't picked for the final competition.
   - ○ She has to cook sausage and she's a vegetarian.
   - ○ She has no ingredients.

2. Who is Crandon?
   - ○ Virginia's annoying younger brother
   - ○ another cook competing against Virginia on the cooking show
   - ○ Virginia's best friend
   - ○ one of the judges on the cooking show

3. Bratwurst is a type of
   - ○ dessert.
   - ○ cheese.
   - ○ vegetable.
   - ○ sausage.

4. Virginia has two scouting badges for
   - ○ making campfires and cooking on campfires.
   - ○ roasting marshmallows and swimming.
   - ○ cooking and singing.
   - ○ being on TV and cooking.

5. Who wins the cooking competition?
   - ○ Crandon wins.
   - ○ Virginia wins.
   - ○ They tie.
   - ○ They are both disqualified.

Writing

6. The title “Broccoli and Bratwurst” is an example of

- ○ a simile.
- ○ alliteration.
- ○ a metaphor.
- ○ rhyme.

7. In the sentence on page 92, “I had dazzled the judges with my meatless dishes,” *dazzled* means

- ○ stunned.
- ○ dazed.
- ○ impressed.
- ○ angered.

8. Which sentence is punctuated correctly?

- ○ “Yes, Crandon. Very clever!” I said flatly.
- ○ “Yes Crandon very clever!”, I said flatly.
- ○ Yes, Crandon. Very clever! I said flatly.
- ○ “Yes, Crandon. Very clever! I said flatly.

9. In the phrase on page 94, “I whirled into action,” *whirled* means

- ○ started working quickly.
- ○ stopped to think about what to do.
- ○ started working.
- ○ ordered others to do the work.

10. The line on page 94, “I was a tornado, tearing through everything I had to get done.” uses

- ○ a pun.
- ○ a simile.
- ○ a metaphor.
- ○ alliteration.

Answers are on pages 116 to 117.

Reading

1. Describe how Virginia solves her problem.

2. Do you think Crandon believes he will win the cooking contest? Support your answer.

3. Describe Virginia's character. You might choose to create a drawing in response to this question.

Answers are on page 117.

Writing

4. Create a menu for a cookout. Think of at least three dishes you might serve.

5. Imagine you are Crandon. Retell this story from his point of view.

Answers are on page 117.

Falling

Short Story written by Diane Robitaille

"Six times six is thirty-six," my brother says. "Six times seven is ..."

"MOM!" I yell. "Make Eddie STOP!"

"Eddie, Edie, quit it!" Mom yells back from the kitchen.

Mom is fixing dinner. Eddie and I (I'm Edie) are doing homework in the dining room. Or I'm trying to. Who can do homework when someone else—Eddie—does his homework out loud?

Eddie falls silent.

I take my books into the kitchen just to get away from Eddie for a minute. I show Mom the story I'm writing, and she smiles.

Eddie and I are twins. I don't know why Mom thought naming us Eddie and Edie would be a good idea. It's not. But there are a lot of bad ideas right now. We're in the same grade at school, with the very same teachers. We're in the same sports. We have to do our homework together and help each other. And I'm not supposed to complain about Eddie. That's a bad idea right there!

If I complain, Mom will just remind me how close we were when we were babies. "You were as close as two peas in a pod," she'll say.

So I don't say anything. I go back right away to be with Eddie. He can't help being a nuisance. And I do love him a lot. He's my twin brother.

This is the thing about twins: Twins are always together when they're young. Most twins are.

Eddie and I were always together too, for a long time.

And then Eddie fell, when he was three years old. He fell out of a window that shouldn't have been open. And he was in hospital for almost a year.

He finally came home. But he was different. I guess I was different too. Sure, we saw each other a lot that year he was in hospital. I visited him often. Not every day, but most days.

But something happened. Maybe it happened in the fall. Maybe it happened when he was in hospital all that time, mostly all by himself.

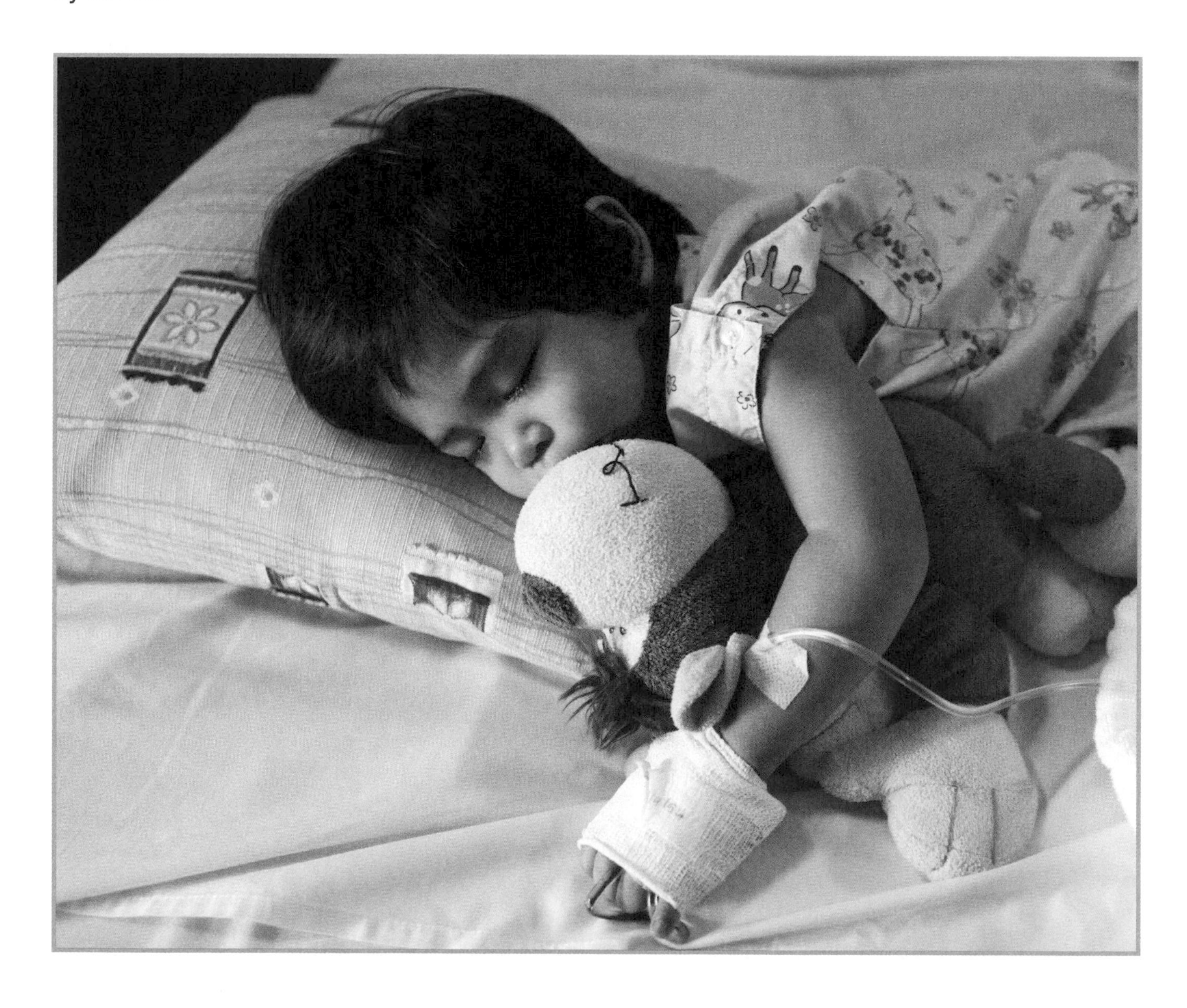

Eddie doesn't dream anymore. That's what the doctors say. They've watched him while he sleeps, that's how they can be so sure.

So I know he doesn't dream about falling or about his time in the hospital.

I do. Every night, I dream about the open window. About falling. About hitting the ground three floors below.

This is the thing about twins: Twins aren't like other brothers and sisters. The bond they have is tighter, stronger, bigger. That's what everyone says. And I know the bond I have with Eddie is the strongest bond I have with anyone.

So maybe my dreams are really what Eddie would dream, if he still could.

I go back to the dining room, and I move his pencil back to where Eddie can reach it.

He's muttering under his breath now. He's up to "Nine times nine is eighty-one."

I hug him as I walk by. He's my twin brother.

Reading

1. What is Edie's problem?
   - ○ She doesn't like her brother.
   - ○ Her mother won't listen to her.
   - ○ She cares a lot for her brother, but she feels like he can sometimes be a nuisance.
   - ○ She has too much homework.

2. Where is this story set?
   - ○ long ago, in ancient Rome
   - ○ in the future, in a spaceship
   - ○ in the present, in a family's home
   - ○ in the present, in a shopping mall

3. Why is the story called "Falling"?
   - ○ because Eddie fell out of a window
   - ○ because Eddie falls asleep and dreams
   - ○ because Edie dreams of an open window
   - ○ because Edie falls asleep and dreams

4. What does Edie want the reader to understand about twins?
   - ○ that twins argue a lot
   - ○ that twins are often in the same class
   - ○ that twins usually look alike
   - ○ that twins share a tight bond

5. How is Edie most likely feeling at the end of the story?
   - ○ happy she's finished her homework
   - ○ sad that she can't have dinner yet
   - ○ angry that her brother is talking
   - ○ glad that she still has a brother

Writing

6. Choose the sentence that is written correctly.
   - ○ Eddie and me are twins.
   - ○ Eddie and I are twins.
   - ○ Eddie and I is twins.
   - ○ Me and Eddie are twins.

7. In the sentence on page 105, “He’s muttering under his breath now,” *muttering* means
   - ○ speaking in a low voice.
   - ○ repeating himself.
   - ○ yelling.
   - ○ ranting.

8. Which sentence uses a simile?
   - ○ Nine times nine is eighty-one.
   - ○ You were as close as two peas in a pod.
   - ○ Twins aren’t like other brothers and sisters.
   - ○ So maybe my dreams are really what Eddie would dream, if he still could.

9. Which of the following sentences is **NOT** using a contraction?
   - ○ Eddie’s books are on the floor.
   - ○ Eddie doesn’t dream anymore.
   - ○ “Eddie’s bugging me,” I said.
   - ○ We’re not like other siblings.

Answers are on page 117.

Reading

1. Describe Edie and Eddie's relationship. Support your response with information from the text and your own ideas.

2. At the beginning of the story, do you think the mother is being fair to Edie? Support your answer.

Answers are on page 117.

Writing

3. Write a letter to Edie from Eddie. What do you think Eddie wants to tell his sister?

4. Write a letter back to Eddie from Edie. How do you think Edie will respond to her brother's letter?

Answers are on page 117.

Answers

The answers for open-response questions are **sample answers only**. Your responses may vary. The EQAO expectation for an open-response question is that it will

- address all aspects of the question fully.
- use specific and relevant details, information, or ideas from the selection.
- communicate ideas clearly.
- use the conventions of spelling, punctuation, and grammar correctly.

The Babysitter's Start-Up Guide

Multiple Choice

1. an article about how to become a babysitter
2. preparedness and responsiblity
3. helps you determine your availability.
4. you might want to babysit older children.
5. may have time for homework while babysitting.
6. bored.
7. the introduction of a list.
8. but
9. verb

Open Response

1. Babysitting is a rewarding job because it gives you the opportunity to make some extra money while spending time with children. Spending time and playing games with children is fun and entertaining. The time that you are working will pass quickly. Also, it is rewarding because you are making children happy.
2. Babysitting is not for everyone. Some people do not enjoy spending time with children. Other people may be too busy and have no time to babysit. Also, a person who is not responsible or mature will make a bad babysitter.
3. Answers will vary. Check that the story clearly includes story elements such as character, setting, plot, problem, and resolution.

What Is Electricity?

Multiple Choice

1. a nonfiction article about electricity
2. Rubber is an insulator.
3. Plastic covers prevent direct contact with electricity.
4. metal
5. It shows the flow of electricity from a battery, through a switch, to a light bulb.
6. need.
7. ownership/possession.
8. This is the Dynamo Room in the Edison Electric Lighting Station in New York City.
9. Before electricity, people used oil lamps or candles for light and did little work after sunset.

Open Response

1. Inside a car is a battery that stores electricity. The electricity in a car's battery creates sparks that start the gasoline burning. The burning gasoline is what makes the engine start and then the wheels move. Also, there are parts of the car that run only on electricity, for example, the headlights, turn signals, radio, and dashboard instruments.
2. Electricity travels from the power plants to our houses through wires that hang from poles. Sometimes, trees grow close to these wires. Windstorms can cause trees to fall. If a tree is near these wires, it can fall on the wires causing them to break or disconnect. Electricity needs a linked path to travel to its destination. If the wires are no longer attached, the electricity will stop at the gap.
3. Electricity is mostly generated in power plants. Attached to these power plants are high-power

transmission lines that run through tall towers. The lines carry electricity to substations that are located near the places that use the electricity. From the substations, electricity moves in overhead and underground wires that are attached to the school.

4. I would keep a flashlight and batteries in my kit so that I could see in the dark. Candles and matches might also be useful, but you'd have to be careful with them. A radio that runs on batteries would also be useful in the kit so that my family can get any updates on the power outage. I'd also keep a family first-aid kit in case of injuries during the power outage.

Energy in the Future

Multiple Choice

1. pollutes Earth's environment.
2. turn the Sun's energy into electricity.
3. the country is located on a coastline with strong and steady winds.
4. changing the engines in cars so they can burn alternative fuels
5. resourceful.
6. sunlight
7. For over a century, the gas we use in cars came from crude oil or petroleum.
8. irregular.

Open Response

1. Renewable energy sources continuously renew themselves, and non-renewable energy sources take Earth millions of years to replace once they have been used up. Wind power, solar power, and water (hydro) power are examples of renewable energy sources because they can be reused and we do not run out of them. Coal, gas, and oil are examples of non-renewable energy sources. These are all sources of energy that can only be used once.
2. Hydro power is good for the environment because it doesn't pollute the air. On the other hand, hydro power is also bad for the environment because hydro dams can damage the environment by changing where water flows. This harms plants and animals.
3. Hydrogen might be considered the "wonder fuel of the future" because there is a large amount of water in the world. Also, hydrogen gas is clean; it doesn't cause pollution.
4. I think it is important for scientists to continue developing alternative energy technologies because many of the technologies that are currently being used depend on non-renewable energy sources. Sources such as oil and gas will get all used up, and once they are gone we will not be able to use them again. Also, many of the energy sources being used today still create pollution and cause many problems for the environment.

Up, Up, and Away!

Multiple Choice

1. turn the burners on.
2. a container that carries passengers
3. is made of tough, but light, materials
4. create a variety of envelopes.
5. how a hot-air balloon rises.
6. to sink
7. On clear summer mornings, people enjoy going hot-air ballooning with friends.
8. recreation.
9. effortless.

Open Response

1. Wind direction and strength cannot be controlled and also may be unpredictable. Wind can change suddenly, and heavy wind conditions can cause sharp movements and make it difficult to fly safely.

2. Helium and hot-air balloons are similar because they both have lift and the ability to float in the air. They also use a gas in the envelope that is lighter than the gas outside the envelope. They are different because hot-air balloons use hot air inside the envelope, while helium balloons use helium gas to float. Helium gas is lighter than air, and unlike hot-air balloons, helium balloons do not need a source of heat such as a gas burner. Also, helium balloons can fly much higher than hot-air balloons.
3. Answers will vary. Check that the story has a clear setting, characters, and problem.

Engineering a Spacesuit

Multiple Choice

1. astronauts need spacesuits because of extreme temperatures.
2. timer, blocks, camera, and winter gloves
3. loss of feeling in their hands
4. on Mars
5. the gloves of a spacesuit.
6. correctly.
7. 2
8. 2, 1, 4, 3
9. enclose a definition for the word *prototypes*.

Open Response

1. The gloves of a spacesuit are awkward and hard to use. Astronauts lose feeling in their hands after working a long time on a spacewalk. Engineers are trying to make the gloves with different materials to fix this problem.
2. I think the activity is included to make the text more interesting and show children how hard it is to work with gloves on.
3. The engineers had to consider temperature when designing the EMU because there is a huge range of temperatures in space. In space, direct sunlight can reach 120 °C, which is incredibly hot. Away from the sunlight, the temperature can drop below –100 °C, which is incredibly cold.
4. Answers will vary. Check that the journal entry includes facts and ideas suggested by the text.

Solving the Puzzle of Global Warming

Multiple Choice

1. without greenhouse gases, Earth would be very cold.
2. rising greenhouse gases are caused by humans.
3. hurricane activity is intensifying.
4. released by the use of fossil fuels.
5. buying less stuff.
6. 3
7. Our school has many electrical devices: phones, computers, televisions, and fans.
8. decreasing.
9. cooling.

Open Response

1. Polar bears hunt for ring seals that are out on the ice. This occurs usually from May to early July because during this time the ice is solid. Since global warming has caused the ice to melt and break up earlier, the polar bears are not getting enough time to hunt for ring seals. If the polar bears are unable to hunt for ring seals, they will starve, become unhealthy, and produce fewer cubs.
2. The diagram helps the reader understand what global warming is because it offers a detailed explanation of the greenhouse effect with pictures to help the reader visualize what is happening.
3. I can help solve the global warming issue by reducing the amount of energy that I use. For example, the water in my house is heated by an electric water heater. If I take shorter showers, this will reduce the amount

of electricity that is used. I also could buy fewer products and try to reuse what I have. Another way I can help is by recycling paper, plastics, and metal. Using less paper means fewer trees will be cut down—trees and other plants help reduce global warming. And creating new products requires lots of energy, so it makes sense to recycle.

4. Answers will vary. Check that the letter includes a date, salutation, and sign-off, as well as details about why the scientist's visit is important.

Sisterlist

Multiple Choice

1. argument
2. nicely, became
3. because it has a rhythm and some of the lines rhyme
4. to endure something difficult.
5. Don't act like a little kid.
6. it is a proper noun.
7. shame.
8. deserve
9. "Don't start whining that you are bored."
10. That is.

Open Response

1. The mother uses the word *brick* because she feels the older sister is helpful and reliable when it comes to supporting and helping the family. The mother is comparing the sister to a brick, a material that is strong and dependable.
2. When the mother is around, the older sister acts as if she really cares for her younger sister. She tells her sister that she loves her and will take her out and around the town. Once the mother leaves the house, the sister's attitude completely changes, and she tells her younger sister that she doesn't like her. She explains to her sister that she is only taking care of her because she is getting paid to do so. She goes into great detail, telling her sister all the things she is not allowed to do while they are together. She even threatens her little sister.
3. Answers will vary. Check that feelings and the younger sister's perspective are expressed clearly.

Little Red, the Hood

Multiple Choice

1. because she is trespassing
2. wildflowers
3. the police.
4. an undercover agent.
5. all of the above
6. to be cheated.
7. scam.
8. discovered, walking
9. innocently
10. made up.

Open Response

1. The wolf trusts Little Red because she is a good actor. Little Red gives the impression that she is naive and trusting by blinking her big blue eyes and acting innocent. She convinces the wolf that she is going to report the money to the police and that she is too nervous to spend large amounts of money.
2. Throughout the story the wolf is clearly excited over the idea of getting Little Red's money. When he first sees the basket of money, the text says that a little prickle of excitement runs down his back to the tip of his tail. When Red agrees to make the trade, his heart begins to pound.
3. Answers will vary. Check that the paragraph begins with a topic sentence and includes supporting details.

The Journal of Rose Marie Smithson

Multiple Choice

1. job
2. Rose Marie's growth and blacksmithing ability.
3. an illness.
4. Rose Marie fears her high voice will give away her secret.
5. in the 1830s, in La Prairie, Lower Canada
6. multiple statements that share a close connection.
7. an adjective.
8. though, or
9. shocked.

Open Response

1. In this text, there are events that did actually occur, but there are also fictional characters. For example, Rose Marie Smithson may not have been a real person, but in the early to mid-1800s girls could not become smithy apprentices, and at that time a railway was built in Canada.
2. The period between January 27, 1835, and October 11, 1835, is a difficult time for Rose Marie. Her journal entries focus on her father's poor health and the family's poverty. Rose Marie stresses the difficulties they are facing in her entries: "I am so afraid," "we are running short of food," "we have no money," and "I wish his health would improve." These comments help the reader understand how terrible life is for the family.
3. I think if they discover that Rose Marie is a girl, the other workers will make sure she is fired. Also, I think her friendship with Thomas will end because he will be angry about her deception. On the other hand, maybe Thomas will stand up for her and make sure she is treated well and gets to keep her job.
4. Answers will vary. Check that the journal entries are similar in voice and format to the original.

Who Stole Grandma's Pie?

Multiple Choice

1. pumpkin
2. a mystery story.
3. in the fridge
4. to emphasize the word.
5. Sammy
6. It's, its
7. a verb
8. troubled.
9. greatest

Open Response

1. Sammy thinks his grandma claimed that the pie went missing so he would come and visit her. In the story, Sammy realizes when he hugs his grandma that he has not seen her in a while, so there is a good chance that she missed him and wanted to see him.
2. Gloria Ketchum and her daughter aren't suspects because they didn't need to steal the pie. Grandma explains that she had invited Gloria over to the house for some pie and tea. Gloria brought her daughter, and Grandma gave each of them a piece of pie. They would have no reason to steal any pie because they had already had some.
3. Answers will vary. Check that the story makes sense, that the mystery is clearly developed, and that any dialogue is punctuated correctly.

Broccoli and Bratwurst

Multiple Choice

1. She has to cook sausage and she's a vegetarian.
2. another cook competing against Virginia on the cooking show
3. sausage.
4. making campfires and cooking on campfires.
5. Virginia wins.
6. alliteration.

7. impressed.
8. "Yes, Crandon. Very clever!" I said flatly.
9. started working quickly.
10. a metaphor.

Open Response

1. Virginia solves her problem by thinking about all the ingredients she has available and how she can use those ingredients to make a vegetarian sausage. She doesn't give up. She works quickly to make them and does such a good job that she wins.
2. Yes, I think that he believes he will win because he feels like the expert at cooking meat and cooking with fire. He even boasts to Virginia that it will be "wurst" for her. No, I think he knows that Virginia is the better cook. That's why he starts crying when he realizes he doesn't even have everything ready on time.
3. Virginia is smart and determined. She's a good cook and competitive. She thinks about different ways a problem can be solved. She's hard-working.
4. I would serve veggie burgers on a bun with tomato slices; grilled mushroom and eggplant kebobs; and grilled pineapple with ice cream.
5. Answers will vary. For example: I was competing on a cooking show against Virginia the Vegetarian. She had really impressed the judges. But so had I. I had made some really good dishes. It was mean of Virginia to call me Crandon the Carnivore. She's a year older than me, so she should really be more thoughtful. And she didn't have to laugh at me when all my bratwurst got burnt because my fire was too high and too hot.

Falling

Multiple Choice

1. She cares a lot for her brother, but she feels like he can sometimes be a nuisance.
2. in the present, in a family's home
3. because Eddie fell out of a window
4. that twins share a tight bond
5. glad that she still has a brother
6. Eddie and I are twins.
7. speaking in a low voice.
8. You were as close as two peas in a pod.
9. Eddie's books are on the floor.

Open Response

1. Edie and Eddie are twins. Edie loves her brother a lot, but she can sometimes be annoyed because she has to help him.
2. Yes, I think the mother is being fair. Edie should help take care of her brother; the mother can't do everything and can't be with him all the time. It's good that Edie has all the same classes as Eddie; that way he won't feel alone. No, I think the mother is making Edie be responsible for something the mother should be responsible for. If Eddie needs help, an adult should be there to help him.
3. Answers will vary. For example:

   July 14, 2018

   Dear Edie,

   Thank you so much for always taking care of me. I really like that we go to class together and go to sports together. It makes me feel like I did when we were younger.

   I know I sometimes annoy you. You know I can't help it. You are so good to me. I don't know what I would do without you.

   All my love,

   Eddie
4. Answers will vary. For example:

   July 17, 2018

   Dear Eddie,

   Thank you for your letter. It means a lot to me that you would thank me for everything I do.

   I know you can't help being annoying sometimes. Don't worry. I'll always love you. I don't know what I'd do without you, too!

   Love, your sister,

   Edie

Test Tips

The following tips will help you be successful on the EQAO Literacy Test.

Reading Selections

1. Read each selection carefully. Think about what you are reading. Use reading strategies such as visualizing or making connections.
2. Think about the details in the text. For fiction selections, you might be asked questions about the setting, characters, or plot. For nonfiction selections, you might be asked questions about the main idea or about supporting details. As you read, identify these aspects of a selection.
3. Reread each selection. Focus on any parts of the text that you might not have understood the first time. Underline key details.

Answering Questions

1. Read each question carefully. Think about what it is asking.
2. Ask yourself: Do I know the answer now? Should I skim the selection looking for the answer?
3. Look in the selection for key words from the question.
4. For multiple-choice questions, think about each possible answer. Which answer is the *best* response to the question? If you're not sure, review the selection. Cross out any answers that you know for sure are not correct.
5. For open-response questions, make sure you understand the question. Skim the selection, looking for details to support your response.
6. If you don't know an answer, move on to the next question. If you have time, return to that question.
7. Always review your answers.

COMPLETION CERTIFICATE

CONGRATULATIONS!

You have completed the *Nelson EQAO Grade 6 Reading and Writing Workbook*!

Presented to:

____

Date:

____

GREAT JOB!